READING READINESS

un

ap

Print the missing letters.

A B C D

F _ H _ J

K L _ N O

_ Q _ S _

_ U V _ X _ Z

Print the letter that comes **after.**

Print the letter that comes **before.**

Draw lines to match the uppercase letters to the lowercase letters.

Aa Bb

A B C D E F

d a c b f e

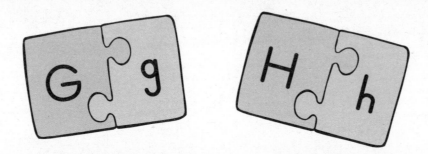

G H I J K L

k i g j l h

Draw lines to match the uppercase
letters to the lowercase letters.

M N O P Q R S

o r n p s m q

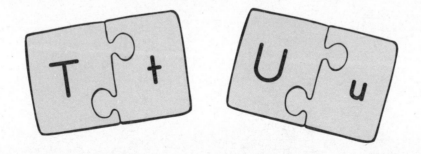

T U V W X Y Z

v x t z y w u

Say the name of each picture.
Print the first letter you hear in each word.
Read the word.

___og   ___at   ___at

___ish   ___oat   ___ite

Say the name of each picture.
Print the first letter you hear in each word.
Read the word.

_oon   _est   _ig

_ug   _un   _op

Say the name of each picture.
Print the letter **a** to finish each word.
Read the word.

f l ___ g

b ___ t

f ___ n

b ___ l l

c ___ t

c ___ p

Say the name of each picture.
Print the letter **e** to finish each word.
Read the word.

h___n   n___st   ___gg

Say the name of each picture.
Print the letter **i** to finish each word.
Read the word.

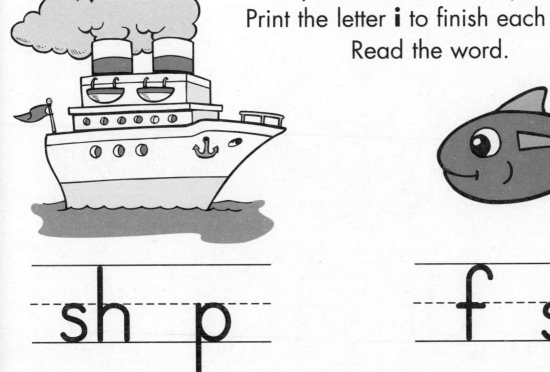

sh___p   f___sh

Say the name of each picture.
Print the letter **o** to finish each word.
Read the word.

l ___ g   fr ___ g   m ___ p

Say the name of each picture.
Print the letter **u** to finish each word.
Read the word.

r ___ g   dr ___ m   c ___ p

Car and **bear** have the same ending sound.
Say the name of the first picture in each row.
Circle the pictures in each row that have
the same ending sound.

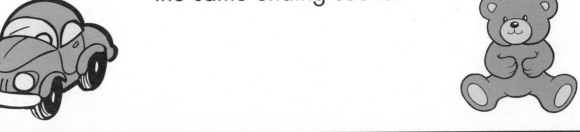

Say the name of the first picture in each row.
Circle the pictures in each row that have
the same **ending** sound.

Look at each picture.
Say the word. Print the word.

Cat rhymes with **hat**.
Say the name of each picture.
Circle the pictures
in each group that rhyme.

Draw lines to connect the things that rhyme.

The pictures tell a story.
Write a **1** in the box with the picture that shows what happens first. Use the numbers **2, 3,** and **4** to put the rest of the story in order.

Say the name of each object. Print the missing letters.

arn

un

ow

est

orse

ig

oat

og

at

Say the name of each object. Print the missing letters.

Print your favorite words.

Say the name of each object. Print the missing letters.

Print your favorite words.

Say the name of each object. Print the missing letters.

Print your favorite words.

Say the name of each object. Print the missing letters.

Print your favorite words.

Short a makes the sound of a in apple.

Say the name of each object. Print the missing letters.

apple

h __ t

c __ n

p __ n

c __ t

m __ t

f __ n

22

Color all the short **a** words red.

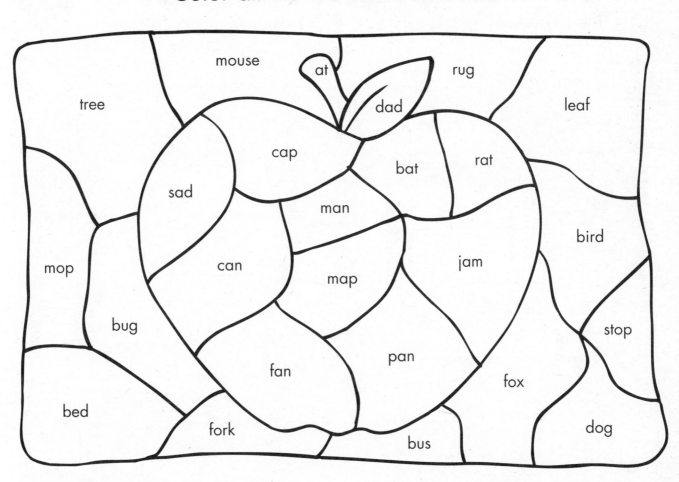

mouse   at   rug

tree   dad   leaf

cap

sad   bat   rat

man

mop   can   jam   bird

map

bug   stop

fan   pan   fox

bed   fork   bus   dog

Print some short **a** words.

Short e makes the sound of e in vest.

Say the name of each object. Print the missing letters.

vest

t_nt

h_n

b_nch

gg

n_st

Use the short e words to finish the puzzle.

Word bank:
bench, fence, ten, tent, hen, vest

Look at each picture. Print the words in the puzzle.

Across: ⇒

② [rooster]   ④ [tent]   ⑤ [fence]

Down: ⇓

① [vest]   ③ [bench]   ④ **10**

Short i makes the sound of i in bib.

Say the name of each object. Print the missing letters.

bib

w   g

p   g

GIGANTIC

sh p

f sh

Print your favorite words.

Short o makes the sound of o in the word top.

Say the name of each object. Print the missing letters.

top

fr__g

p__nd

l__g

r__ck

Print your favorite words.

Short u makes the sound of u in nut.

Say the name of each object. Print the missing letters.

nut

Print your favorite words.

Color all the short u words yellow.

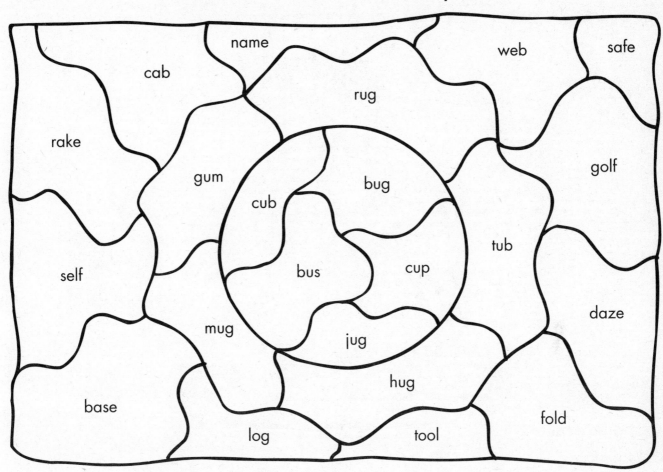

Print some short u words.

_____

- - - - - - - - - - - - - - - - - - - -

_____

- - - - - - - - - - - - - - - - - - - -

_____

- - - - - - - - - - - - - - - - - - - -

_____

b, c, f, h, m, p, s, fl

Print new rhyming words by adding letters
to the beginning of **at**. Use the letters above.

bat

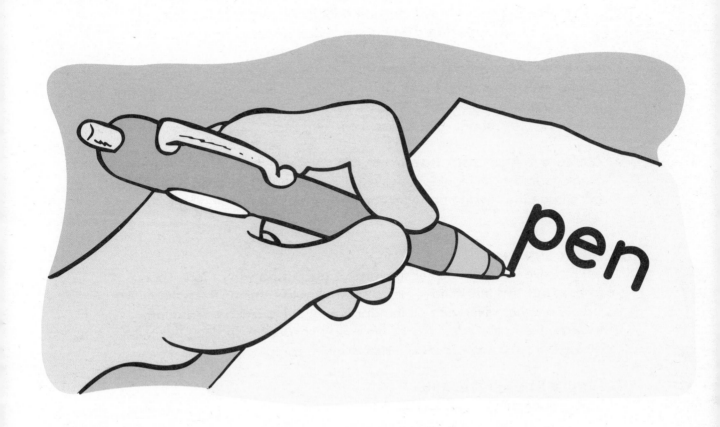

d, h, m, p, t

Print new rhyming words by adding letters
to the beginning of **en**. Use the letters above.

pen

Fun Family Activities

The following activities will provide additional review of the concepts explored on the workbook pages.

1. Look for Same and Different
Take a walk around the house with the child. Look for objects that are the same: a pair of roller skates, a stack of dinner plates, cushions on the couch, etc. Talk about what makes them the same.

2. Make an Alphabet Book
Staple together 26 blank pages. Write one alphabet letter on each page. Encourage the child to draw on each page a picture beginning with that letter sound.

3. Make Patterns
Set the silverware on the kitchen table. Create a pattern of fork, spoon, fork, spoon. Ask the child to place silverware to continue the pattern. Create another silverware pattern for your child to extend. Gradually increase the pattern difficulty as the child experiences success, but always provide at least two complete patterns in the sample.

4. Play a Rhyming Game
Say a word and have the child say a word that rhymes with your word. Take turns calling out the words.

5. Read a Story
Begin reading a storybook to the child. After you read a few pages, ask the child to predict what will happen next. After you finish reading, discuss how the ending of the story could be different. Write the child's new story ending on a piece of paper and let the child draw a picture to illustrate it.

6. Reward Stickers
Use reward stickers to celebrate a job well done. You or the child can choose when to place a sticker on a specific page. Use a sticker as a reward when the child completes a page that requires extra care or is a little more difficult. The child can choose to place stickers on pages he or she is proud of completing.